2 Eins, zwei, drei ... (Seiten 10–11)

1 The bank has sent texts to customers with their c[...]
maths problems in German to work out the PINs. [...]
new PIN below the phone.

1

Meine Bank

zehn – acht = _zwei_

vier + drei = _sieben_

zwei + drei = _____

fünf + eins = _____

2 7 _ _

2

Meine Bank

sechs + zwei = _____

zehn – neun = _____

sieben – drei = _____

eins + vier = _____

_ _ _ _

3

Meine Bank

sieben – vier = _____

acht + eins = _____

drei + sechs = _____

fünf + zwei = _____

_ _ _ _

2 Write the winning lottery numbers in words.

1 **13** _____

2 **11** _____

3 **16** _____

4 **18** _____

5 **12** _____

6 **17** _____

3 Write two sentences for each speaker. Give the
speaker's age and the age of his/her friend.

er ist = he is

sie ist = she is

1

13 12

Ich bin dreizehn Jahre alt. _____

Sie ist zwölf Jahre alt. _____

2

15 17

_____
_____

3

14 16

_____
_____

Stimmt! 1 © Pearson Education Limited 2013

3

1 Read the dialogue and complete the table with the correct forms of each verb.

Melanie: Hallo! Ich heiße Melanie. Wie heißt du?

Marco: Ich heiße Marco. Ich wohne in Straubing. Wo wohnst du?

Melanie: Ich wohne in Braunschweig. Wie alt bist du?

Marco: Ich bin zwölf Jahre alt. Wer ist das?

Melanie: Sie heißt Jessie. Sie wohnt in Leipzig und ist dreizehn Jahre alt.

wer = who

	heißen (to be called)	**wohnen** (to live)	**sein** (to be)
ich (I)		wohne	
du (you)			bist
er/sie/es (he/she/it)	heißt		

2 Write the missing word in each sentence and complete the crossword.

```
1        W □ □ □ □
2        O □ □ □ □ □
3        L □ □ □ □
4    □ □ □ F □
5    □ □ □ S □ □ □ □ □ □ □
6        B □ □ □ □ □ □ □
7      □ □ U □ □ □ □ □ □ □
8      □ □ R □ □ □
9        G □ □ □ □ □
```

bist   zwölf

wohne   wohnst

Jahre

Schottland

Deutschland

geht's

alt

1 Ich _____ in Manchester.

2 Wo _____ du, Nick?

3 Wie _____ ist er?

4 Er ist _____ Jahre alt.

5 Glasgow ist in _____ .

6 Wie alt _____ du?

7 Ich wohne in Berlin. Das ist in

_____ .

8 Ich bin elf _____ alt.

9 Wie _____ ?

3 Research why the city of Wolfsburg is important to Germany.

4 Meine Welt ist wunderbar! (Seiten 14–15)

Übungsheft B

KAPITEL 1

1 The printer has made four mistakes labelling the illustrations. Write *richtig* or *falsch* under each caption.

1 Ich bin musikalisch.

_____

4 Ich bin kreativ.

_____

2 Ich bin sehr launisch.

_____

5 Ich bin laut.

_____

3 Ich bin ziemlich freundlich.

_____

6 Ich bin lustig.

_____

2 Rewrite the false captions from exercise 1, correcting them so that they are true.

_____

_____

_____

_____

> faul
> lustig
> musikalisch
> sportlich

3 Separate out the words to form three sentences.

meinelieblingsfußballmannschaftistbayernmünchen

meinlieblingssportisttennis

meinelieblingszahlistsieben

> ! Remember that each sentence must start with a capital letter. Also, remember that nouns start with a capital letter.

1 _____

2 _____

3 _____

4 Write a sentence about your favourite ...

1 football team: _____

2 sport: _____

3 number: _____

Stimmt! 1 © Pearson Education Limited 2013

5 Meine Sachen (Seiten 16–17)

1 **Write the German question word under its English translation.**

Who?	What?	How?	Where?	Where from?

Wie? Was?
Wo? Woher?
Wer?

2 **Write the correct question word in each question. You may use each word more than once.**

1 _____ bist du? Sportlich?

2 _____ wohnt Shiva?

3 _____ heißt du?

4 _____ kommst du?

5 _____ ist das? Ist das Max?

6 _____ alt ist Michael?

7 _____ ist Hannover? *Hannover ist in Deutschland!*

8 _____ ist deine Lieblingsmusik?

3 **Read the paragraph below. Pretend that you're Gabi, and answer each question in a complete German sentence.**

> *Hallo! Ich heiße Gabi und ich bin vierzehn Jahre alt. Ich wohne in Kiel, in Deutschland, aber ich komme aus Swansea. Das ist in Wales. Wie bin ich? Ich bin sportlich, lustig und auch sehr laut! Mein Lieblingsmonat ist Dezember und meine Lieblingssendung ist ‚Die Simpsons'. Ich habe ein iPad und auch einen Computer. Tschüs!*

1 Wie heißt du? _____

2 Wo wohnst du? _____

3 Woher kommst du? _____

4 Wie bist du? _____

5 Wie heißt deine Lieblingssendung? _____

6 Was hast du? _____

6 Ich über mich (Seiten 18–19)

1 Complete the table with the correct words.

	the	a	my	your
masculine: Sport				
feminine: Musik				
neuter: Auto				

2 Write each sentence or question in German. Tick the boxes when you've checked each part of your work.

> Part of writing accurately in any language is going back over your work to check that there aren't any mistakes. Get into the habit now and watch both your English and German improve!

1 I'm called Osman.

_____

2 I live in Germany.

_____

3 I'm quite friendly and also creative.

_____

_____

4 I have a mobile phone.

_____

5 Where do you live?

_____

☐ Spelling of key phonics sound 'ei'

☐ Name has a capital

☐ Spelling of key phonics sound 'eu'

☐ Full stop at the end

☐ Check the qualifier

☐ Check the connective

☐ Capital on the noun

☐ Right word for 'a'

☐ Correct question word

☐ Verb in second position

3 Write a short paragraph about yourself. Use the sentences in exercise 2 as prompts. Check your work against the checklist below.

☐ genders   ☐ qualifiers   ☐ connectives   ☐ verbs

☐ capital letters   ☐ spelling   ☐ question words

_____

_____

1 Fill in the gaps by writing the German for the words in brackets.

Hallo! Ich _____ (am called) Marie und ich _____ (live)

in Walsrode. Das ist in _____ (Germany). Ich

bin fünfzehn _____ (years) alt. Ich bin _____ (very)

sportlich und _____ (quite) intelligent, _____ (but)

ich bin _____ (also) faul. Mein _____

(favourite sport) ist Hockey und _____ (my) Lieblingsmusik

ist Pop. Ich _____ (have) einen Vogel aus Amerika. Er ist

_____ (very) freundlich, aber _____ (not) laut!

2 Crack the code and write the sentences correctly.

a 18/24/19   4/12/19/13/22   18/13   20/28/7/7/18/13/20/22/13

   Ich wohne in Göttingen.

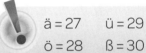

| ä = 27 | ü = 29 |
| ö = 28 | ß = 30 |

b 22/9 18/8/7   20/26/13/1   21/9/22/6/13/23/15/18/24/19

_____

c 14/22/18/13/22   15/18/22/25/15/18/13/20/8/14/6/8/18/16

18/8/7   14/12/1/26/9/7

_____

_____

3 Make up a coded sentence in German for a classmate to solve. Don't forget to provide a key.

4 Write the questions you would ask to get these answers.

1   _Wie heißt du?_ _____

Ich heiße Elaine.

2 _____

Mein Lieblingssport ist Tennis.

3 _____

Sami ist musikalisch und intelligent, aber sehr launisch.

4 _____

Alwin ist vierzehn Jahre alt.

1 Read the website entries.

 Ich heiße **Franzi** und suche Freunde aus England, Irland oder Nordirland. Ich habe eine Schlange zu Hause! Sie ist sechs Jahre alt. Ich wohne in Wien. Das ist in Österreich. Ich bin sehr kreativ und intelligent! Schreib mir bitte!

 Hallo! Ich heiße **Hannah** und ich wohne in London, in England. Ich lerne Deutsch. Ich suche Freunde aus Deutschland, Österreich und auch aus der Schweiz. Ich bin sportlich und spiele Fußball und auch Tennis, aber ich bin sehr faul! Meine Lieblingsmusik ist Rock. Schreib mir!

 Mein Name ist **Felix** und ich wohne in der Schweiz, aber ich komme aus Dortmund in Deutschland. Zu Hause habe ich eine Wii und mein Lieblingsspiel ist FIFA. Meine Lieblingsfußballmannschaft ist Bayern-München. Ich suche Freunde aus Schottland und Wales.

 Hi! Ich bin **Muhammad** und ich wohne in Cardiff. Das ist in Wales. Ich bin sechzehn Jahre alt. Meine Lieblingssache ist Technologie. Ich habe zu Hause einen Computer, ein Handy und auch ein iPad. Ich bin nicht sehr sportlich, aber sehr freundlich. Mein Lieblingsland ist Deutschland und ich suche dort Freunde.

Write the name of the person who ...

1 is looking for friends from Switzerland.   _Hannah_

2 supports a football team.   _____

3 has a pet.   _____

4 is just looking for friends from Germany.   _____

5 lives in a different place from where they were born.   _____

6 does not particularly like sport.   _____

7 lives in Switzerland.   _____

> **suche** = seek
> **Schreib mir (bitte)!** = Write to me (please)!
> **dort** = there

2 Write your own profile for the website. Use as much German as you can from *Kapitel 1* to describe yourself.

_____

_____

_____

_____

Grammatik (Seiten 22–23)

1 Write a sentence using the correct German word for 'a' for each item.

1 **2** **3** **4** **5** **6** **7** **8**

1 _Das ist ein Computer._

2 _____

3 _____

4 _____

5 _____

6 _____

7 _____

8 _____

> die Gitarre   das Handy
> der iPod   der Computer
> das Skateboard   das Keyboard
> der Fußball   die Wii

> **Grammatik**
> masculine – *ein*
> feminine – *eine*
> neuter – *ein*

2 Circle the correct verb form to complete each sentence.

1 Lukas **habe / hat / hast** einen Computer.

2 Ich **heiße / habe / hat** einen Vogel zu Hause.

3 Wo **bist / ist / wohnst** er?

4 Er **ist / komme / bin** musikalisch und sportlich.

5 Julia **bin / ist / wohnt** fünfzehn Jahre alt.

6 Wie alt **wohnst / bist / bin** du?

7 Wo **hast / bist / bin** ich?

> **Grammatik**
> You can use the pronouns
> *er* ('he') or *sie* ('she') instead
> of writing someone's name.
> Both need the *er/sie/es* form
> of the verb.

3 Complete the table with the correct forms of each regular verb.

wohnen (to live)	**kommen** (to come)	**heißen** (to be called)
ich *wohne*	ich	ich
du	du *kommst*	du
er/sie/es	er/sie/es	er/sie/es *heißt*

Now use the table to write the correct verb in each gap.

1 Mein Handy _____ aus China.

2 Meine Schlange _____ Sissel.

3 Du _____ Gabi.

4 _____ du aus Berlin?

5 _____ Monika in Hamburg?

6 Deine Lieblingssendung

_____ ,EastEnders'.

7 Ich _____ Wolfgang.

8 Wo _____ du?

Mein Fortschritt

1 Record your levels for *Kapitel* 1.

2 Look at the level descriptors on pages 59–60 and set your targets for *Kapitel* 2.

3 Fill in what you need to do to achieve these targets.

Listening	I have reached Level _____ in **Listening**.
	In *Kapitel* 2, I want to reach Level _____
	I need to _____
	_____
	_____
	_____
Speaking	I have reached Level _____ in **Speaking**.
Hallo!	In *Kapitel* 2, I want to reach Level _____
	I need to _____
	_____
	_____
	_____
Reading	I have reached Level _____ in **Reading**.
	In *Kapitel* 2, I want to reach Level _____
	I need to _____
	_____
	_____
	_____
Writing	I have reached Level _____ in **Writing**.
	In *Kapitel* 2, I want to reach Level _____
	I need to _____
	_____
	_____
	_____

Hallo! • Meeting and greeting

Wie heißt du?	*What's your name?*
Ich heiße ...	*My name is ...*
Hallo!	*Hello! / Hi!*
Guten Tag!	*Hello!*
Wie geht's?	*How are you?*
Gut, danke. Und dir?	*Fine, thanks. And you?*
Nicht schlecht.	*Not bad.*
Tschüs!	*Bye!*
Auf Wiedersehen!	*Goodbye!*

Die Zahlen 1–19 • Numbers 1–19

eins	*1*
zwei	*2*
drei	*3*
vier	*4*
fünf	*5*
sechs	*6*
sieben	*7*
acht	*8*
neun	*9*
zehn	*10*
elf	*11*
zwölf	*12*
dreizehn	*13*
vierzehn	*14*
fünfzehn	*15*
sechzehn	*16*
siebzehn	*17*
achtzehn	*18*
neunzehn	*19*
Wie alt bist du?	*How old are you?*
Ich bin ... Jahre alt.	*I am ... years old.*
Wie alt ist (Julia)?	*How old is (Julia)?*
(Julia) ist ... Jahre alt.	*(Julia) is ... years old.*

Wo wohnst du? • Where do you live?

Ich wohne in ...	*I live in ...*
Er/Sie/Es wohnt in ...	*He/She/It lives in ...*
... England	*England*
... Irland	*Ireland*
... Nordirland	*Northern Ireland*
... Schottland	*Scotland*
... Wales	*Wales*
... Deutschland	*Germany*
... Österreich	*Austria*
... der Schweiz	*Switzerland*

Wie bist du? • What are you like?

Ich bin ...	*I am ...*
Er/Sie ist ...	*He/She is ...*
faul	*lazy*
freundlich	*friendly*
intelligent	*intelligent*
kreativ	*creative*
launisch	*moody*
laut	*loud*
lustig	*funny*
musikalisch	*musical*
sportlich	*sporty*

Wörter

Lieblingssachen • Favourite things

Mein Lieblingssport ist …
My favourite sport is …

Mein Lieblingsmonat ist …
My favourite month is …

Meine Lieblingsmusik ist …
My favourite music is …

Meine Lieblingszahl ist …
My favourite number is …

Meine Lieblingssendung ist …
My favourite programme is …

Meine Lieblingsfußballmannschaft ist …
My favourite football team is …

Mein Lieblingsspiel ist …
My favourite game is …

Mein Lieblingsland ist …
My favourite country is …

Mein Lieblingsauto ist …
My favourite car is …

Was ist dein Lieblingssport?
What's your favourite sport?

Was ist deine Lieblingszahl?
What's your favourite number?

Was ist dein Lieblingsland?
What's your favourite country?

Fragewörter • Question words

Wie?	*How?*
Was?	*What?*
Wo?	*Where?*
Woher?	*Where … from?*
Wer?	*Who?*

Oft benutzte Wörter • High-frequency words

und	*and*
(und) auch	*(and) also*
aber	*but*
sehr	*very*
ziemlich	*quite*
nicht	*not*
Was denkst du?	*What do you think?*
Ich denke, …	*I think …*
Ich auch!	*Me too!*
Ich nicht!	*Not me!/That's not what I think!*
Was? Du spinnst!	*What? You're joking!*

Hast du einen Computer? • Have you got a computer?

Ich habe …	*I have …*
einen Computer	*a computer*
einen iPod	*an iPod*
einen Fußball	*a football*
eine Gitarre	*a guitar*
eine Wii	*a Wii*
eine Schlange	*a snake*
ein Handy	*a mobile phone*
ein Keyboard	*a keyboard*
ein Skateboard	*a skateboard*

1 Extreme Haustiere (Seiten 30–31)

1 Complete the sentences about the pets. Write the correct words in the gaps. Remember to think about the gender of each animal.

1 Ich habe __ein__ Pferd. __Es__ ist groß und heißt Romeo.

2 Ich habe _____ Kaninchen. _____ ist niedlich und heißt Timmo.

3 Ich habe _____ Katze. _____ ist intelligent und heißt Mieze.

4 Max hat _____ Schlange. _____ ist zwei Jahre alt.

5 Gabi hat _____ Pferd. _____ ist launisch.

6 Ich habe _____ Hund. _____ ist freundlich und heißt Prinz.

7 Susi hat _____ Goldfisch. _____ heißt Nemo.

> ### Grammatik
> Remember: after *haben* the masculine word for 'a' changes from *ein* to *einen*.

> ### Grammatik
> m. der / ein → **er**
> f. die / eine → **sie**
> n. das / ein → **es**

2 Tina Tierfan has lots of pets! Write Tina's answers to the interviewer's questions about how many of each animal she has.

> ### Grammatik
> Hund (-e)   Pferd (-e)
> Katze (-n)   Goldfisch (-e)
> Schlange (-n)   Maus (Mäuse)

1 Hast du einen Hund? _Nein! Ich habe drei Hunde._____

2 Hast du ein Pferd? _____

3 Hast du eine Katze? _____

4 Hast du einen Goldfisch? _____

5 Hast du eine Schlange? _____

6 Hast du eine Maus? _____

2 supertiere (Seiten 32–33)

1 Complete the sentences about the animals. Write the correct name in each gap.

Hermann   Minnie   Sisi

Kizzi   Moto   Millie

1 _____ ist schnell.   **4** _____ ist superintelligent.

2 _____ ist süß.   **5** _____ ist cool.

3 _____ ist gemein.   **6** _____ ist kräftig.

2 Write a sentence to say what each of the *Supertiere* can do.

1 Hermann   **2** Sisi   **3** Minnie   **4** Kizzi   **5** Millie   **6** Moto

1   Hermann kann springen. _____

2 _____

3 _____

4 _____

5 _____

6 _____

> **Grammatik**
> The verb *kann* is always followed by an infinitive verb.

3 Read the text below, then translate it into English.

> Günther Goldfisch ist mein Lieblingstier. Er ist ein Jahr alt. Er ist sehr lustig und kräftig, aber auch ziemlich süß. Er kann schwimmen, springen und auch im Aquarium tanzen! Günther hat einen Freund: er ist sehr cool und schlau.

1 Find the numbers in the puzzle, and write them next to the correct numeral.

v	i	e	r	u	n	d	s	e	c	h	z	i	g	m	e
b	a	l	c	o	e	z	n	f	w	i	r	d	s	k	s
s	e	c	h	s	u	n	d	d	r	e	i	ß	i	g	a
q	g	n	a	j	n	x	i	n	d	m	h	t	g	ü	o
h	a	c	h	t	u	n	d	f	ü	n	f	z	i	g	i
u	e	i	n	u	n	d	a	c	h	t	z	i	g	p	b
n	t	e	r	i	d	f	b	n	ß	e	d	z	g	d	s
d	r	e	i	u	n	d	v	i	e	r	z	i	g	w	e
e	v	h	f	r	e	a	m	ß	p	l	s	j	a	q	c
r	d	r	e	i	u	n	d	z	w	a	n	z	i	g	h
t	z	a	n	j	n	x	o	u	e	y	g	r	e	v	z
k	c	p	f	s	z	d	l	b	n	l	a	i	h	m	i
i	b	z	w	e	i	u	n	d	s	i	e	b	z	i	g
a	g	b	n	ü	g	y	i	a	z	o	m	e	d	h	e

100 _____

64 _____

99 _____

43 _____

72 _____

36 _____

58 _____

81 _____

60 _____

23 _____

2 Describe each of the families. Fill in the gaps for the first family. Write the whole description for the second family.

42   7   Tom 14   5

Oban

47   51   Katja 12   10   19

Köln

Ich heiße Tom. Ich bin vierzehn Jahre alt. Es gibt vier Personen in meiner Familie. Meine Mutter ist _____ Jahre alt. Ich habe einen Bruder. _____ ist _____ Jahre alt. Ich habe eine Schwester. _____ ist _____ Jahre alt. Wir wohnen in _____ .

_____

_____

_____

_____

_____

_____

3 Write about your family (real or imaginary). Use the descriptions in exercise 2 to help you.

der **Stiefbruder** = stepbrother
die **Halbschwester** = half-sister
Ich bin Einzelkind. = I am an only child.

1 Describe each person's hair and eyes.

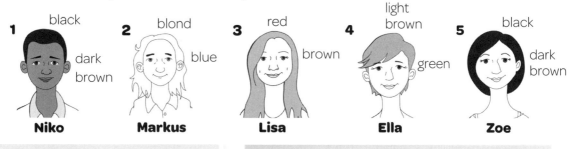

1 black / dark brown — **Niko**
2 blond / blue — **Markus**
3 red / brown — **Lisa**
4 light brown / green — **Ella**
5 black / dark brown — **Zoe**

Grammatik
When you describe hair and eyes, the adjectives (colour, length) need an **e** on the end.

hell = light   **hellbraun** = light brown
dunkel = dark   **dunkelblau** = dark blue

1 Er heißt Niko. Er hat kurze, schwarze Haare und dunkelbraune Augen.

2 _____

3 _____

4 _____

5 _____

2 Complete the text by choosing the correct words from the cloud to fill the gaps. There are more words than you need.

Es gibt fünf _____ in meiner Familie. Wir _____ in Braunschweig. Das ist in

_____ . Meine _____ heißt Emma und sie ist neunundvierzig

_____ alt. Sie ist sehr freundlich und hat _____, schwarze Haare. Mein

Vater _____ auch neunundvierzig und er hat kurze, dunkelbraune Haare und

braune _____ .

Ich habe zwei _____ : einen Bruder und eine Schwester. _____ Bruder

heißt Mehmet und er ist _____ Jahre alt. Er ist launisch aber _____ lustig.

_____ Schwester, Isla, hat grüne Augen und _____ Haare. Sie ist sechzehn

Jahre alt, sehr klein und _____ .

*Deutschland   alt   Augen   Personen
braune   wohnen   sportlich   Meine
Mutter   Jahre   lange   Geschwister
zwölf   auch   Mein   blau   ist*

Read the text for gist first. For each sentence, think about whether you need a noun, a verb, a connective or an adjective.

5 Alles Gute! (Seiten 38–39)

1 Reorder the words to make correct sentences. Don't forget the full stop!

1 (am) (Mai) (Ich) (Geburtstag) (habe) (neunzehnten)

_____

2 (hat) (Oktober) (am) (Oma) (Geburtstag) (elften) (Meine)

_____

3 (Geburtstag) (Stiefbruder) (Dezember) (am) (Dein) (dritten) (hat)

_____

4 (hast) (Geburtstag) (einunddreißigsten) (Juli) (Du) (am)

_____

5 (und) (Geburtstag) (haben) (achten) (am) (Michael) (Juni) (Monika)

_____

2 Complete each sentence by writing the date. Write each holiday in English.

01.01. Neujahr ist am _ersten Januar_____ . _New Year_____

01.05. Der Maifeiertag ist am _____ . _____

03.10. Der Tag der Deutschen Einheit ist am _____ _German Unity Day_

_____ .

25.12. Weihnachten ist am _____ . _____

31.12. Silvester ist am _____ . _____

3 Read the short profile about Yannic and write a summary in the table.

> Er heißt Yannic Spiller. Er ist dreizehn Jahre alt und kommt aus Trier. Trier ist in Deutschland. Yannic hat am siebten Januar Geburtstag. Er hat einen Bruder, Tim. Tim ist achtzehn Jahre alt. Yannic hat auch eine Schwester. Sie heißt Steffi und ist sechzehn Jahre alt. Die Familie Spiller hat zwei Haustiere: einen Hund und eine Katze.

Name:		Geschwister:	
Alter:			
Wohnt in:		Haustiere:	
Geburtstag:			

4 Now write a short profile about yourself.

1 Rescue the question words from the alphabet soup. Write each one on a line and use it to write a question.

Wie viele Brüder hast du?

_____

_____

_____

_____

_____

_____

wer wo ~~wie viele~~ wann was woher wie

2 The police have written a summary about a crime suspect. Write six questions for a journalist to ask the suspect. The questions should cover all the information in the summary.

1 _Wie heißt du?_

2 _____

3 _____

4 _____

5 _____

6 _____

Martin Kolwitz ist 24 Jahre alt. Er hat am achten November Geburtstag. Er wohnt in Hamburg, in Deutschland. Er hat einen Bruder. Er hat auch Haustiere: zwei Hunde.

 Remember: the verb usually goes straight after the question word.

3 Use these notes to write questions to Martin about his accomplice, Sophie.

1 _Wie heißt sie?_

2 _____

3 _____

4 _____

5 _____

Sophie Meyer
19
Ebbingen, Deutschland
Haare – kurz, Augen – blau
Geb. 21.10.

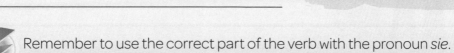 Remember to use the correct part of the verb with the pronoun _sie_.

4 Write a summary about Sophie, like the one the police wrote about Martin in exercise 2.

Wiederholung 1

1 **Complete the sentences. Choose the correct word from the cloud to fill in each gap.**

1 _____ Mutter ist sehr freundlich und intelligent.

2 Hast du _____ Meerschweinchen?

3 Wir haben _____ Haustier.

4 Wo ist _____ Vogel?

5 Ich habe _____ Bruder.

> dein   kein
>
> ein   meine
>
> einen

2 **You are describing pets at a pet show. Use the owners' notes to write what sort of pet they have, what the pet is like and what it can do.**

Mareike

> mouse
> Pippa
> cute, fast
> fly, swim

Mareike hat _____ .

Sie heißt _____ .

Sie ist _____ .

Sie kann _____ .

Aaron

> cat
> Mieze
> intelligent, cool, mean
> jump, play football

_____ .

_____ .

_____ .

_____ .

3 **Decscribe the animal you'll be entering in the pet show by writing a similar description.**

Example: Ich habe ...

Wiederholung 2

1 Read the texts below.

Hallo! Ich heiße **Anna** und ich bin fünfzehn Jahre alt. Ich habe am elften Februar Geburtstag. Ich wohne in Klagenfurt, in Österreich. Ich bin ziemlich groß und schlank und habe kurze, schwarze Haare und blaue Augen. Ich habe keine Geschwister – ich bin Einzelkind. Ich habe einen Goldfisch und einen Wellensittich. Ich kann Flöte spielen und Italienisch sprechen.

Hi! Ich bin **Noah** und ich komme aus Aachen. Das ist in Deutschland. Ich habe am zweiten November Geburtstag und bin vierzehn Jahre alt. Ich liebe Haustiere! Ich habe zwei Hunde, drei Katzen und eine Maus. Ich habe eine große Familie. Ich habe einen Halbbruder (er ist ein Baby) und zwei Schwestern. Mein Halbbruder ist sehr süß und klein. Er hat schwarze Haare und blaue Augen.

a Complete the sentences by writing *Anna* or *Noah*.

1 _____ lives in Austria.

2 _____ can play the flute.

3 _____ 's birthday is on the 02.11.

4 _____ has a half-brother.

5 _____ is 15 years old.

6 _____ has cats.

b Write *richtig* or *falsch* next to each statement.

1 Anna hat einen Halbbruder. _____

2 Anna kann auch Englisch sprechen. _____

3 Noahs Halbbruder hat blaue Augen. _____

4 Klagenfurt ist nicht in Deutschland. _____

5 Anna hat am fünfzehnten Februar Geburtstag. _____

6 Anna hat keine Geschwister. _____

2 Translate these sentences into German.

1 My birthday is on the first of May. _____

2 She can speak German. _____

3 My guinea pig is very cute. _____

4 Your sister has light blue eyes. _____

5 My grandparents live in Southampton.

_____

6 My brother can fly.

_____

1 Complete the table by writing the correct form of *haben* for each pronoun.

> haben hast
> habt hat
> habe
> haben

! Words for 'you':
du (speaking to one family member or friend)
ihr (speaking to two or more family members or friends)
Sie (speaking to people you don't know or adults)

ich	du	er/sie/es	wir	ihr	Sie/sie

Now complete the sentences with the correct form of *haben*.

1 Katja, _hast_ du eine Katze?

2 Tom und Niko, _____ ihr einen Hund?

3 _____ Sie eine Schlange, Herr Brand?

4 Ich _____ ein Pferd.

5 Frau Gerber, _____ Sie eine Maus?

6 Herr Alexander _____ ein Pferd.

2 Join each pronoun to a verb. There is more than one possible verb for some of the pronouns. Then write a question or a sentence with each pair.

1 ich   **a** macht   **1** _____

2 du   **b** heißen   **2** _____

3 er   **c** wohnst   **3** _____

4 wir   **d** heiße   **4** _____

5 ihr   **e** spielt   **5** _____

6 Sie   **f** spielen   **6** _____

3 Rewrite the sentences so they include the verb *kann*.

1 Mein Bruder fliegt.   _Mein Bruder kann fliegen._

2 Ich spiele Flöte.   _____

3 Meine Mutter schwimmt.   _____

4 Mein Vater springt.   _____

5 Ich tanze.   _____

6 Er singt gut.   _____

1 Record your levels for *Kapitel* 2.

2 Look at the level descriptors on pages 59–60 and set your targets for *Kapitel* 3.

3 Fill in what you need to do to achieve these targets.

Listening	I have reached Level _____ in **Listening**. In *Kapitel* 3, I want to reach Level _____ I need to _____ _____ _____ _____
Speaking Hallo!	I have reached Level _____ in **Speaking**. In *Kapitel* 3, I want to reach Level _____ I need to _____ _____ _____ _____
Reading	I have reached Level _____ in **Reading**. In *Kapitel* 3, I want to reach Level _____ I need to _____ _____ _____ _____
Writing	I have reached Level _____ in **Writing**. In *Kapitel* 3, I want to reach Level _____ I need to _____ _____ _____ _____

Haustiere • Pets

Hast du ein Haustier?	*Have you got a pet?*
Ich habe ...	*I have ...*
einen Goldfisch	*a goldfish*
einen Hamster	*a hamster*
einen Hund	*a dog*
ein Kaninchen	*a rabbit*
eine Katze	*a cat*
eine Maus	*a mouse*
ein Meerschweinchen	*a guinea pig*
ein Pferd	*a horse*
eine Schlange	*a snake*
einen Wellensittich	*a budgie*
kein Haustier	*no pet*

Eigenschaften • Qualities

Wie ist er/sie/es?	*What is he/she/ it like?*
Er/Sie/Es ist ...	*He/She/It is ...*
dick/schlank	*fat/thin*
frech/niedlich	*cheeky/cute*
gemein/süß	*mean/sweet*
groß/klein	*big/small*
kräftig	*strong*
schlau	*cunning*
(super)lustig	*(really) funny*
Er/Sie/Es kann ...	*He/She/It can ...*
Italienisch sprechen	*speak Italian*
fliegen	*fly*
Flöte/Fußball/Wii spielen	*play the flute/ football/on the Wii*
(schnell) laufen	*run (fast)*
lesen	*read*
Rad fahren	*ride a bike*
schwimmen	*swim*
singen	*sing*
springen	*jump*
tanzen	*dance*

Die Zahlen 20–100 • Numbers 20–100

zwanzig	*twenty*
dreißig	*thirty*
vierzig	*forty*
fünfzig	*fifty*
sechzig	*sixty*
siebzig	*seventy*
achtzig	*eighty*
neunzig	*ninety*
hundert	*hundred*
einundzwanzig	*twenty-one*
zweiundzwanzig	*twenty-two*

Meine Familie • My family

Es gibt ... Personen in meiner Familie.	*There are ... people in my family.*
meine Mutter	*my mother*
mein Vater	*my father*
mein Bruder	*my brother*
mein Stiefbruder/ Halbbruder	*my stepbrother/ half-brother*
meine Schwester	*my sister*
meine Stiefschwester/ Halbschwester	*my stepsister/ half-sister*
meine Eltern	*my parents*
meine Großeltern	*my grandparents*
Hast du Geschwister?	*Have you any brothers and sisters?*
Ich habe zwei Brüder.	*I have two brothers.*
Ich habe drei Schwestern.	*I have three sisters.*
Ich bin Einzelkind.	*I'm an only child.*
Ich habe keine Geschwister.	*I have no brothers and sisters.*

Wörter

Die Farben • Colours

schwarz	*black*
weiß	*white*
grau	*grey*
braun	*brown*
rot	*red*
orange	*orange*
gelb	*yellow*
grün	*green*
blau	*blue*
indigoblau	*indigo*
violett	*violet*
lila	*purple*
rosa	*pink*
bunt	*brightly coloured*
hellblau/dunkelblau	*light blue/dark blue*

Haare und Augen • Hair and eyes

Er/Sie hat ...	*He/She has ...*
schwarze/braune/ blonde/rote Haare	*black/brown/ blond/red hair*
kurze/lange/ mittellange Haare	*short/long/ mid length hair*
blaue/braune/grüne/ graue Augen	*blue/brown/green/ grey eyes*

Die Monate • The months

Januar	*January*
Februar	*February*
März	*March*
April	*April*
Mai	*May*
Juni	*June*
Juli	*July*
August	*August*
September	*September*
Oktober	*October*
November	*November*
Dezember	*December*

Das Datum • The date

Wann hast du Geburtstag?	*When is your birthday?*
am 1. (ersten) Januar	*on 1 January*
am 3. (dritten) Februar	*on 3 February*
am 7. (siebten) März	*on 7 March*
am 8. (achten) April	*on 8 April*
am 15. (fünfzehnten) Mai	*on 15 May*
am 29. (neunund- zwanzigsten) Juni	*on 29 June*
Ich habe (heute) Geburtstag.	*It's my birthday (today).*

Oft benutzte Wörter • High-frequency words

und	*and*
aber	*but*
oder	*or*
ziemlich	*fairly, quite*
sehr	*very*

1 Look at the survey results in the table. Then answer the questions using full German sentences.

	🏸	⚽	🤽	🏀	🏒	🏓	🤾
Ahmed	sehr gern			nicht gern			ziemlich gern
Nicole		sehr gern			nicht gern		
Christa	gern		sehr gern				ziemlich gern
Torsten		nicht gern		sehr gern		gern	
Herr und Frau Meyer	sehr gern			gern	nicht gern	ziemlich gern	

😊😊 = sehr gern 😊 = gern 😐 = ziemlich gern ☹ = nicht gern

1 Wer spielt sehr gern Fußball? <u>Nicole spielt sehr gern Fußball.</u>

2 Wer spielt gern Tischtennis? _____

3 Was spielt Christa sehr gern? _____

4 Was spielen Herr und Frau Meyer gern? _____

5 Wer spielt Basketball nicht gern? _____

6 Wer spielt ziemlich gern Handball? (2) _____

7 Und du? Was spielst du gern? _____

2 Write three questions and three answers about the other people and sports in the table in exercise 1. Use the questions above as a model.

_____

_____

_____

_____

_____

_____

1 Write the words from the cloud in the grid. Translate the code word into English.

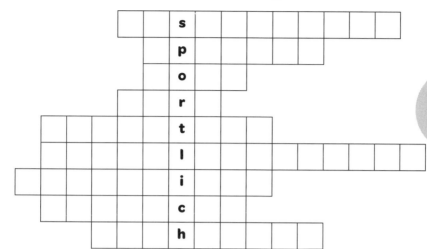

furchtbar

Eishockey

schlecht

spielst

irre

stinklangweilig

langweilig

Tischtennis

toll

2 Read about all the activities Hannes and Lola are involved in. Then write *richtig* or *falsch* next to each statement.

Hallo! Ich heiße **Hannes**. Ich finde Sport fantastisch. Ich spiele Tennis und schwimme. Schwimmen finde ich total super. Ich reite mit meiner Freundin, aber das finde ich langweilig. Fußball finde ich cool. Ich fahre auch gern Skateboard und lese sehr gern Sport- und Fitnessmagazine.

Meine Freundin heißt **Lola.** Sie findet Tischtennis toll. Lola fährt auch gern Rad – das ist sehr gesund! Sie findet schwimmen auch gut, aber Fußball findet sie nervig. Sie kann nicht Ski fahren. Im Winter spielt sie Eishockey und sie sieht sehr gern Eishockey im Fernsehen.

meine Freundin = my girlfriend

gesund = healthy

Fernsehen = television

1 Both Hannes and Lola participate in winter sports. _____

2 Lola watches ice hockey on television. _____

3 Hannes really likes swimming. _____

4 Lola thinks skiing is fantastic. _____

5 Lola plays ice hockey in winter. _____

6 Hannes doesn't enjoying horse riding. _____

7 Lola thinks football is exciting. _____

8 Hannes watches sports programmes on television. _____

Stimmt! 1 © Pearson Education Limited 2013

1 Separate the words to form five time phrases and write them below. Number the phrases in order of frequency, starting with 1 for the most frequent. Translate the phrases into English.

jedenTagdreimalpro WocheeinmalproMonatam Wochenendesechsmalpro Monat

☐ _____   _____

☐ _____   _____

☐ _____   _____

☐ _____   _____

☐ _____   _____

2 Use the time phrases from exercise 1 to answer the questions about yourself. Write your answers in full sentences.

1 Gehst du ins Kino? _____

2 Machst du Sport? _____

3 Gehst du einkaufen? _____

4 Hörst du Musik? _____

5 Spielst du Wii? _____

6 Chillst du mit deinen Freunden? _____

 nie = never

3 Join up the sentence halves. Rewrite each sentence so that it starts with the time phrase.

1 Ich höre am

2 Ich chille am

3 Ich spiele sehr

4 Ich mache jeden

5 Ich esse einmal

6 Ich gehe einmal pro

a Tag Sport.

b Abend Musik.

c pro Woche Pizza.

d Monat ins Kino.

e oft Xbox.

f Wochenende.

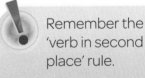 Remember the 'verb in second place' rule.

1 Unscramble and write down the time phrase in each sentence.
Then translate the sentences into English.

> ### Grammatik
> You can use the present tense with a future time phrase to say what you are going to do – just as in English.

1 Wir machen änhcset eoWhc Filme. _nächste Woche_

We are going to make …

2 Ich suche ma Mtanog Infos im Internet. _____

_____

3 Wir sehen ma eneneoWhcd Katzenvideos auf YouTube. _____

_____

4 Ich chatte nejde denbA auf Facebook. _____

_____

5 Stefan spielt ni iezw cnoWhe Wii Sport. _____

_____

6 Ich lade gomrne Musik herunter. _____

_____

2 Underline all the verbs in the text. Circle the words that are in first position in the sentences. Write a sentence about what you notice.

> Hey du!
>
> Franzi hier! Jetzt sind wir Freunde auf Facebook! Jeden Tag spiele ich Wii.
>
> Jede Woche schreibt mein Vater ein Blog, aber das finde ich langweilig.
>
> Am Abend lese ich gern E-Books. Morgen telefoniere ich mit Freunden
>
> in Kanada über Skype. Das finde ich cool! Im Sommer fahren wir nach
>
> Vancouver. Fantastisch! Was machst du am Computer und wie oft?

_____

3 Reply to the question Franzi has asked you in his chat.

Use as many time phrases as you can in your reply.

1 What type of word is needed to fill the gap in each sentence? Complete each sentence by writing an appropriate German word or words in the gap.

verb *noun* *time/frequency phrase* *connective* *adjective*

Type of word

1 Ich _finde_ Tennis toll.   _verb_

2 Meine Schwester findet Tischtennis _____ .   _____

3 Wir sehen _____ fern.   _____

4 Herr Peters spielt nächste Woche Tennis _____ Fußball.   _____

5 Mein Bruder schreibt ein _____ .   _____

2 Answer the questions about German grammar.

Use the sentences in exercise 1 to help you answer these questions.

1 Where in a sentence do verbs usually go?

_____

2 What often goes after a verb? _____

3 What can you expect to go after *ein/eine*? _____

4 Which German verb suggests you're giving an opinion? _____

3 Replace the underlined word(s) with something else: a different noun, adjective or time phrase.

1 Ich finde Tischtennis <u>furchtbar</u>. _Ich finde Tischtennis langweilig._

2 Ich spiele nicht gern <u>Fußball</u>. _____

3 Micha spielt gern <u>Wii</u>. _____

4 Er macht <u>einmal pro Monat</u> Judo. _____

5 Olli findet E-Books <u>fantastisch</u>. _____

6 Ich sehe <u>jede Woche</u> fern. Meine Schwester sieht <u>jeden Tag</u> Videos auf YouTube.

_____

Remember that you'll keep the reader's interest if you use a variety of different words and phrases.

4 **Write about your friends' hobbies.**

Remember to include:
- opinions
- connectives
- time/frequency phrases
- 'verb in second place' rule

Wiederholung 1

1 Put the words in the correct order to make sentences or questions. Don't forget to insert a full stop or question mark.

1 (fern) (gern) (sehr) (Ich) (sehe) _____

2 (einkaufen) (er) (Wochenende) (geht) (Am) _____

3 (Hausaufgaben) (Ich) (Infos) (lese) (die) (für) _____

4 (in) (Wie) (Stadt) (oft) (du) (fährst) (die) _____

5 (Woche) (Kai) (Wasserball) (Nächste) (spielt) _____

6 (herunter) (Videos) (Ich) (lade) (Musik) (und) _____

2 Rewrite each sentence, beginning with a time phrase. Then translate the sentences into English.

1 Ich spiele Volleyball. (at the weekend) _Am Wochenende spiele ich Volleyball._

At the weekend I am going to play volleyball.

2 Er spielt Basketball. (on Monday) _____

_____

3 Du spielst Tischtennis. (every week) _____

_____

4 Rosa spielt Fußball. (today) _____

_____

5 Ich telefoniere mit Sam. (next week) _____

_____

6 Sophie liest das Buch. (tomorrow) _____

_____

3 Underline the regular verbs and circle the irregular verbs.

> Ich spiele nicht gern Tennis. Ich finde Tennis langweilig. Fußball spiele ich dreimal pro Woche. Mein Bruder spielt sehr gern Tennis. Er fährt auch gern Rad. Radfahren findet er toll. Meine Schwester sieht ziemlich gern fern. Meine Mutter liest ziemlich gern. Oft liest sie Blogs im Internet. Ich lese auch oft. Mein Vater fährt gern Ski und spielt Gitarre.

Wiederholung 2

1 Read the email. Find the German for the following words and phrases in the text.

1 I think _____

4 New Zealand _____

2 about _____

5 comedies _____

3 but _____

6 Best wishes _____

Lieber Anish,

wie geht's? Danke für deine E-Mail.

Ich denke, Technologie ist toll. Ich bin sehr oft online. Ich chatte sehr gern mit Freunden auf Facebook. Facebook finde ich super und ich sehe oft Videos über Fußball auf YouTube.

Ich spiele Computerspiele nicht gern, aber ich suche ziemlich oft Infos für die Hausaufgaben. Meine Cousine, Connie, wohnt in Neuseeland und wir telefonieren ziemlich oft über Skype. Kannst du auch über Skype telefonieren?

Ich mache viel Sport mit meinen Freunden: Wir schwimmen zweimal pro Woche und wir spielen am Abend Basketball. Im Winter fahre ich auch Ski.

Ich esse manchmal am Wochenende mit meinen Freunden Pizza, und dann gehen wir ins Kino. Ich sehe gern Komödien. Nächste Woche sehen wir *Skyfall*.

Liebe Grüße,

Tibor

2 Answer the questions in complete German sentences.

1 Spielt Tibor gern Computerspiele? _____

2 Was macht Tibor auf Facebook? _____

3 Wer wohnt in Neuseeland? _____

4 Wie telefoniert Tibor mit seiner Cousine? _____

5 Wie oft schwimmt Tibor? _____

6 Was machen Tibor und seine Freunde am Wochenende?

_____

3 Write a reply to Tibor's email about your hobbies and activities.

1 **Complete the verb table.**

	fahren (to go/travel)	**sehen** (to see)	**lesen** (to read)
ich			
du	fährst		liest
er/sie/es		sieht	
wir			
ihr			
Sie			
sie			

2 **Complete the sentences by writing the correct form of the verb in brackets.**

1 Ich _____ das Auto. (waschen)

2 _____ du gern Mangabücher? (lesen)

3 Er _____ im Schlafzimmer. (schlafen)

4 Thomas _____ nach Stockholm in Schweden. (fahren)

5 _____ du morgen Torsten? (sehen)

6 _____ du eine Schuluniform? (tragen)

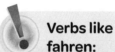

Verbs like fahren:

tragen = to wear
schlafen = to sleep
waschen = to wash

die Schuluniform = school uniform

3 **Write the question for each reply.**

1 _____ Ja, ich spiele Gitarre.

2 _____ Nein, ich spiele nicht gern Wasserball.

3 _____ Ja, Michael schläft im Bett.

4 _____ Ja, ich fahre nach Bremen.

5 _____ Ja, ich lese gern E-Books.

6 _____ Nein, ich sehe nicht gern fern.

7 _____ Ja, ich bin sportlich!

8 Was _____ Ich trage morgen Jeans und ein T-Shirt.

9 _____ Michael trägt eine Schuluniform.

Remember, to form a question you put the verb before the subject:
Du spielst gern Tennis. → Spielst du gern Tennis?

Mein Fortschritt

1 Record your levels for *Kapitel* 3.

2 Look at the level descriptors on pages 59–60 and set your targets for *Kapitel* 4.

3 Fill in what you need to do to achieve these targets.

Listening	I have reached Level _____ in **Listening**. In *Kapitel* 4, I want to reach Level _____ I need to _____ _____ _____ _____
Speaking Hallo!	I have reached Level _____ in **Speaking**. In *Kapitel* 4, I want to reach Level _____ I need to _____ _____ _____ _____
Reading	I have reached Level _____ in **Reading**. In *Kapitel* 4, I want to reach Level _____ I need to _____ _____ _____ _____
Writing	I have reached Level _____ in **Writing**. In *Kapitel* 4, I want to reach Level _____ I need to _____ _____ _____

Wörter

Bist du sportlich?
• Are you sporty?

Ich bin (sehr/ziemlich/ nicht sehr) sportlich.	I am (very/quite/ not very) sporty.
Was spielst du?	What do you play?
Ich spiele ...	I play ...
Ich spiele gern ...	I like playing ...
Ich spiele ziemlich gern ...	I quite like playing ...
Ich spiele nicht gern ...	I don't like playing ... playing ...
Badminton	badminton
Basketball	basketball
Eishockey	ice hockey
Fußball	football
Handball	handball
Tennis	tennis
Tischtennis	table tennis
Volleyball	volleyball
Wasserball	water polo

Was machst du gern?
• What do you like doing?

Was machst du gern?	What do you like doing?
Ich fahre Rad.	I ride my bike.
Ich fahre Skateboard.	I go skateboarding.
Ich fahre Ski.	I ski.
Ich fahre Snowboard.	I snowboard.
Ich lese.	I read.
Ich mache Judo.	I do judo.
Ich mache Karate.	I do karate.
Ich reite.	I go horse riding.
Ich schwimme.	I swim.
Ich sehe fern.	I watch TV.
Ich spiele Gitarre.	I play the guitar.
Ich tanze.	I dance.

Wie findest du das?
• What do you think of it?

Ich finde es ...	I think it's ...
Es ist ...	It's ...
irre	amazing
super	super
toll	great
cool	cool
gut	good
nicht schlecht	not bad
okay	okay
langweilig	boring
nervig	annoying
stinklangweilig	deadly boring
furchtbar	awful

Was machst du in deiner Freizeit?
• What do you do in your free time?

Ich chille.	I chill out.
Ich esse Pizza oder Hamburger.	I eat pizza or hamburgers.
Ich gehe einkaufen.	I go shopping.
Ich gehe ins Kino.	I go to the cinema.
Ich gehe in den Park.	I go to the park.
Ich gehe in die Stadt.	I go into town.
Ich höre Musik.	I listen to music.
Ich mache Sport.	I do sport.
Ich spiele Xbox oder Wii.	I play Xbox or on the Wii.

Stimmt! 1 © Pearson Education Limited 2013

Wörter

Ich bin online • I'm online

Was machst du am Computer?	What do you do on the computer?
Was machst du auf deinem Handy?	What do you do on your mobile?
Ich chatte mit Freunden auf Facebook.	I chat with friends on Facebook.
Ich lade Musik herunter.	I download music.
Ich mache Fotos oder Filme.	I take photos or make films.
Ich sehe Videos.	I watch videos.
Ich simse.	I text.
Ich spiele Computerspiele.	I play computer games.
Ich suche und lese Infos für die Hausaufgaben.	I look for and read information for my homework.
Ich surfe im Internet.	I surf the internet.
Ich telefoniere mit Freunden.	I call my friends.
Ich mache ziemlich viel auf meinem Handy.	I do quite a lot of things on my mobile.

Oft benutzte Wörter • High-frequency words

Wie oft?	How often?
(sehr/ziemlich/ nicht so) oft	(very/quite/not so) often
einmal/zweimal/ dreimal pro Woche/ pro Monat	once/twice/three times a week/ a month
jeden Tag	every day
jeden Morgen	every morning
manchmal	sometimes
immer	always
nie	never
Wann?	When?
am Wochenende	at the weekend
am Abend	in the evening
heute	today
morgen	tomorrow
am Montag	on Monday
nächste Woche	next week
in zwei Wochen	in two weeks

Stimmt! 1 © Pearson Education Limited 2013

1 Ich mag Deutsch! (Seiten 76–77)

1 Write a sentence for each illustration.

1 ___Ich mag_____

2 _____

3 _____

4 _____

5 _____

6 _____

ich liebe	☺☺
ich mag	☺
ich mag … nicht	☹
ich hasse	☹☹

2 Read the forum entries giving people's opinions about school subjects. Then answer the questions below.

> Hallo Leute! Mein Lieblingsfach ist Englisch! Ich liebe Englisch, weil es total interessant ist. Ich lese sehr gern Bücher auf Spanisch und auf Deutsch. Mathe finde ich langweilig. **Pedro**

> Hi Pedro! Ich mag Englisch nicht. Es ist sehr schwierig, aber ich mag Mathe und Naturwissenschaften. Ich finde Mathe supercool. **Nadine**

> Grüezi aus der Schweiz! Ich liebe Theater und Kunst. Ich mag Kunst sehr gern, weil ich total kreativ bin. Informatik finde ich sehr langweilig, und Geschichte und Erdkunde sind nutzlos. **Marta**

Who ...

1 is very creative? _____

2 enjoys reading? _____

3 doesn't like English? _____

4 thinks ICT is boring? _____

5 likes maths? _____

6 can read Spanish? _____

7 loves art? _____

8 doesn't like geography? _____

3 Rewrite each sentence in exercise 1, adding *weil* and an opinion. Use the examples in exercise 2 to help you with word order.

2 Was und wann? (Seiten 78–79)

1 Look at the timetable. Write *richtig* or *falsch* next to each statement.

	Montag	Dienstag	Mittwoch	Donnerstag	Freitag
8.15	Mathe	Erdkunde	Englisch	Deutsch	Technik
9.15	Englisch	Informatik	Theater	Mathe	Deutsch
10.45	Kunst	Mathe	Deutsch	Kunst	Naturwissenschaften
11.45	Naturwissenschaften	Mathe	Naturwissenschaften	Geschichte	Theater
13.30	Deutsch	Sport	Technik	Musik	Englisch

vor = before   **nach** = after   **die Doppelstunde** = double period

1 Am Mittwoch habe ich Deutsch. _____

2 Wir haben am Freitag nach der Pause Technik. _____

3 Am Montag vor der Pause haben wir Englisch. _____

4 Theater ist am Mittwoch und am Donnerstag. _____

5 Ich habe am Donnerstag nach der Mittagspause Musik. _____

6 Am Dienstag habe ich eine Doppelstunde Mathe. _____

2 At what time do you have the following subjects? Write a sentence for each.

1 _Ich habe Englisch um neun Uhr zehn._ _____ 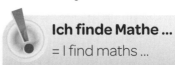 `09:10`

2 _____ `10:05`

3 _____ `11:15`

4 _____ `12:10`

5 _____ `13:20`

6 _____ `14:15`

um acht Uhr = at 8 o'clock

3 Look at the timetable in exercise 1 and describe one school day. Try to add interest to your sentences by giving opinions about some subjects.

Example: Am Montag um acht Uhr fünfzehn
habe ich Mathe. Ich mag Mathe,
weil es interessant ist.

Ich finde Mathe ...
= I find maths ...

1 Write a description for each of the teachers.

1 Mein Sportlehrer heißt Herr Huber.

Er ist cool, aber sehr unpünktlich.

2 _____

_____

3 _____

_____

4 _____

_____

Herr Huber

Frau Schuster

1914–1918

HA! HA!

Frau Klein

Herr Rocher

Use some qualifiers in your descriptions: *sehr, zu, ziemlich, ein bisschen, nicht*

2 Complete the text by writing the correct word from the cloud in each gap.

Mein _____ an der Schule ist Geschichte, _____ meine

Geschichtelehrerin sehr lustig ist! Sie _____ nur ein Haustier, aber ihr

Haustier ist eine Schlange!

Am _____ und am Freitag haben wir Kunst. Ich finde Kunst ziemlich

langweilg, weil es schwierig_____ . Mein Kunstlehrer _____

Herr Ackermann. _____ Schwester ist auch Kunstlehrerin an

meiner _____ ! Sie heißt Frau Ackermann! Meine Sportlehrerin ist

_____ freundlich. Sie heißt Frau Krause und _____

Lieblingssport ist Volleyball. Ich mag Sport,

weil ich sehr _____ bin.

> heißt   hat   Mittwoch   Lieblingsfach   ist
> sehr   Schule   Seine   sportlich   weil   ihr

3 Write the correct word for 'his' or 'her' in each sentence.

1 _____ Bruder lernt Hindi. (his)

2 _____ Schwester ist Lehrerin. (her)

3 _____ Hobby ist Gitarre spielen. (his)

4 _____ Lieblingsfach ist Kunst. (her)

5 _____ Schuluniform ist fantastisch. (his)

6 _____ Bruder ist 19 Jahre alt. (her)

Grammatik

sein = his   **ihr** = her (for masculine and neuter nouns)

seine = his   **ihre** = her (for feminine nouns)

Check the gender of the noun if you are unsure.

1 **Draw a simple picture to show where each of these things is.**

1 Der Musiklehrer ist im Klassenzimmer.
2 Das Buch ist neben dem Computer.
3 Das Poster ist an der Wand.

4 Der Stuhl ist auf dem Tisch und neben der Tür.

1	2	3	4
		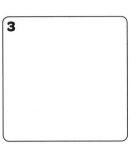	

2 **What is there in the classroom? Start each sentence with *Es gibt* (there is/there are). Write the numbers as words.**

12 _Es gibt zwölf Tische im Klassenzimmer._

6 _____

24 _____

2 _____

4 _____

5 _____

Look at the vocabulary on page 47 for the plurals of the nouns.

3 **Answer the questions using the information in the pictures.**

@peta_ush Darfst du dein Handy in der Schule benutzen?

_____

@tara_winkel Darfst du im Klassenzimmer schnell laufen?

_____

@e_atch Darfst du in der Pause Musik hören?

_____

@janet_mc Darfst du dein Handy in der Mittagspause benutzen?

_____

ich darf   du darfst   er/sie/es darf

5 Mein Lieblingstag (Seiten 84–85)

1 Most of the verbs you've seen end in –*en* in the infinitive. Write the infinitive form of each verb in the table. Then try to work out its meaning from the context.

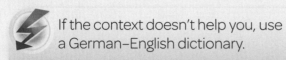 If the context doesn't help you, use a German–English dictionary.

verb	infinitive	meaning in English
Er **geht** in die Schule.	gehen	to go, to walk
Er **kauft** ein Auto.		
Er **steht** auf dem Tisch.		
Warum **redest** du so schnell?		
Ich **wasche** meinen Hund.		
Ich **nehme** das Buch.		

2 Guess the meaning of these compound nouns by separating out the words. Look up the compound nouns in a dictionary to find their gender and meaning.

The second word in each compound noun gives the gender.

compound noun	word 1	word 2	gender	meaning
Fußballfeld	Fußball		das	
Arbeitstag				
Sporthalle				
Klassenarbeit				
Lehrerzimmer				

3 Now write a short German sentence using each compound noun from exercise 2.

1   _Das Fußballfeld ist sehr grün und ..._

2   _____

3   _____

4   _____

5   _____

Wiederholung 1

1 Mimi's description of her school day is in the wrong time order! Number the sentences 1–6 in the correct order of time.

☐ Ich habe um dreizehn Uhr fünfundzwanzig Musik.

☐ Die Pause beginnt um elf Uhr zehn.

☐ Die erste Stunde beginnt um acht Uhr vierzig.

☐ Der Bus kommt um fünfzehn Uhr siebenundvierzig.

☐ Ich komme um sechzehn Uhr dreißig nach Hause.

☐ Wir haben Mathe um elf Uhr fünfundzwanzig.

2 The school is running 20 minutes late today. Rewrite each of the six sentences in exercise 1 with the time that each activity begins today.

3 Complete the sentences by writing the correct possessive pronoun in each gap.

> **sein** = his (for masculine and neuter nouns)   **seine** = his (for feminine nouns)
>
> **ihr** = her (for masculine and neuter nouns)   **ihre** = her (for feminine nouns)

1 _____ Bruder heißt Pawel und _____ Schwester heißt Aga.

2 _____ Lieblingssport ist Eishockey.

3 _____ Katze ist braun, aber _____ Hund ist weiß.

4 _____ Schule ist in Hannover.

5 _____ Lieblingssport ist Reiten und _____ Lieblingsfach ist Mathe.

6 _____ Computer ist neu.

7 _____ Erdkundelehrerin ist sehr streng.

8 _____ Mutter wohnt in Salzburg, aber _____ Vater wohnt in Wien.

4 Describe where each of the items is located in the classroom.

1 Der Computer _ist auf dem Tisch._

2 Das Poster _____

3 Das Whiteboard _____

4 Der Lehrer _____

5 Der Stuhl _____

6 Die Spinne _____

1 Read the texts. Use your knowledge of vocabulary to help you to find these new phrases. Write each German phrase next to the English.

1 My name is _____

2 her favourite artist

_____

3 unfortunately _____

4 My brother also goes

_____

5 an indoor pool _____

6 a pot plant _____

Hallo! Mein Name ist **Maik** und ich wohne in München, in Deutschland. Meine Schule heißt Mathias Brauer Gymnasium und ich finde sie toll. An meiner Schule lerne ich sehr gern Englisch und Geschichte, aber mein Lieblingsfach ist Kunst. Ich mag Kunst, weil ich total kreativ bin. Ich finde meine Kunstlehrerin auch sehr nett. Sie heißt Frau Weber und ihr Lieblingskünstler ist Dürer.

Ich mag nicht Sport, weil ich nicht sehr sportlich bin. Leider habe ich am Montag und auch am Mittwoch Sport. Morgen spielen wir Tennis. Das finde ich nicht so schlecht.

lernen = to learn

Hallo Leute! Ich heiße **Sabine** und ich wohne in Zürich, in der Schweiz. Meine Schule ist sehr groß. Mein Bruder geht auch auf meine Schule.

Mein Lieblingsfach ist Musik und dieses Fach haben wir am Dienstag in der zweiten Stunde und auch am Donnerstag in der vierten Stunde. Sport mag ich auch, weil der Sportlehrer total lustig ist. Sein Lieblingssport ist Schwimmen und wir haben ein Hallenbad in der Schule. Wir haben Sport am Mittwoch in der fünften Stunde und auch am Freitag in der zweiten Stunde.

Mein Klassenzimmer ist sehr schön. Wir haben zehn Computer, ein Whiteboard neben der Tür, viele Poster an der Wand und eine Topfpflanze am Fenster!

2 Answer the questions about the texts in exercise 1. Write complete sentences in German for your answers.

1 Wie heißt Maiks Schule? _____

2 Was mag Maik? _____

3 Was lernt Maik nicht gern? _____

4 Wann hat Maik Sport? _____

5 Wo ist Zürich? _____

6 Was hat Sabine am Donnerstag in der vierten Stunde?

_____

7 Warum mag Sabine Sport? _____

8 Wo ist die Topfpflanze? _____

1 **Answer the questions in full sentences, using *weil* and the reason given.**

1 Warum magst du Kunst? (it's creative)

  Ich mag Kunst, weil es kreativ ist.

2 Warum magst du Englisch? (it's interesting)

  _____

3 Warum spielst du Tennis? (I'm sporty)

  _____

4 Warum hasst du Sport? (it's difficult)

  _____

5 Warum findest du Erdkunde toll? (it's easy)

  _____

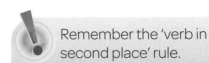

2 **Put the words in the right order to make sentences.**

Remember the 'verb in second place' rule.

1 der in Geschichte dritten wir Stunde haben

  _____

2 habe Pause ich nach der Kunst _____

3 Fußball spiele heute ich _____

4 gibt Klassenzimmer Computer und viele einen es im Poster

  _____

5 Montag ich vierten Stunde habe in am der Mathe

  _____

3 **Write the following school rules in sentences in German.**

Example: Man darf am Montag ...

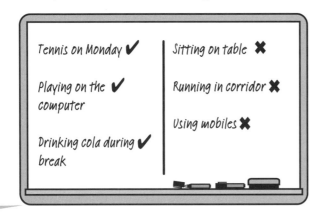

Tennis on Monday ✔

Playing on the ✔
computer

Drinking cola during ✔
break

Sitting on table ✖

Running in corridor ✖

Using mobiles ✖

Man darf is often used to mean 'you/we are allowed to'.

Remember to use the correct preposition and the correct word for 'the' after it.

Mein Fortschritt

1 Record your levels for *Kapitel* 4.

2 Look at the level descriptors on pages 59–60 and set your targets for *Kapitel* 5.

3 Fill in what you need to do to achieve these targets.

Listening	I have reached Level _____ in **Listening**.
	In *Kapitel* 5, I want to reach Level _____
	I need to _____
	_____
	_____
	_____
Speaking	I have reached Level _____ in **Speaking**.
Hallo!	In *Kapitel* 5, I want to reach Level _____
	I need to _____
	_____
	_____
	_____
Reading	I have reached Level _____ in **Reading**.
	In *Kapitel* 5, I want to reach Level _____
	I need to _____
	_____
	_____
	_____
Writing	I have reached Level _____ in **Writing**.
	In *Kapitel* 5, I want to reach Level _____
	I need to _____
	_____
	_____
	_____

Stimmt! 1 © Pearson Education Limited 2013

Wörter

Schulfächer • School subjects

Deutsch	*German*
Englisch	*English*
Erdkunde	*geography*
Geschichte	*history*
Informatik	*ICT*
Kunst	*art*
Mathe	*maths*
Musik	*music*
Naturwissenschaften	*science*
Sport	*sport, PE*
Technik	*technology*
Theater	*drama*

Meinungen • Opinions

mein Lieblingsfach ist ...	*my favourite subject is ...*
ich mag ... (sehr)	*I like ... (a lot)*
ich liebe	*I love*
ich mag ... nicht	*I don't like ...*
ich hasse	*I hate*
gut	*good*
toll	*great*
furchtbar	*awful*
einfach	*easy*
schwierig	*difficult*
interessant	*interesting*
langweilig	*boring*
nützlich	*useful*
nutzlos	*useless*
faszinierend	*fascinating*
nervig	*irritating*
supercool	*really cool*
stinklangweilig	*dead boring*

Die Wochentage • The days of the week

Montag (Mo.)	*Monday*
Dienstag (Di.)	*Tuesday*
Mittwoch (Mi.)	*Wednesday*
Donnerstag (Do.)	*Thursday*
Freitag (Fr.)	*Friday*
Samstag (Sa.)	*Saturday*
Sonntag (So.)	*Sunday*
Was hast du am Montag?	*What do you have on Monday?*
Am Dienstag habe ich ...	*I have ... on Tuesday*
Am Sonntag haben wir keine Schule.	*We have no school on Sunday.*

Die Zeit • Time

Wann?	*When?*
Um wie viel Uhr?	*At what time?*
Um 8:30 Uhr (acht Uhr dreißig).	*At 8:30.*
Wie viel Uhr ist es?	*What time is it?*
Es ist 9:50 Uhr (neun Uhr fünfzig).	*It's 9:50.*
in der ersten Stunde	*in the first lesson*
vor der Pause	*before break*
nach der Mittagspause	*after the lunch break*

Wörter

Eigenschaften • Characteristics

Er/Sie ist …	*He/She is …*
alt	*old*
fair	*fair*
freundlich	*friendly*
jung	*young*
launisch	*moody*
lustig	*funny*
nervig	*annoying*
streng	*strict*
unpünktlich	*unpunctual*

In der Schule • In school

die Lehrerin(-nen)	*teacher (female)*
die Deutsch-lehrerin(-nen)	*German teacher (female)*
der Lehrer(–)	*teacher (male)*
der Sportlehrer(–)	*sports teacher (male)*
Was gibt es?	*What is there?*
Es gibt einen/eine/ein …	*There is a …*
Es gibt viele …	*There are lots of …*
das Klassenzimmer(–)	*classroom*
der Tisch(-e)	*table*
der Stuhl(ˮe)	*chair*
der Computer(–)	*computer*
das Whiteboard(-s)	*whiteboard*
das Poster(–)	*poster*
das Fenster(–)	*window*
die Wand(ˮe)	*wall*
die Tür(-en)	*door*
der Korridor(-e)	*corridor*

Wo ist das? • Where is it?

in der Schule	*in the school*
im Klassenzimmer	*in the classroom*
im Korridor	*in the corridor*
an der Wand	*on the wall*
am Fenster	*by the window*
am Tisch	*at the table*
auf dem Tisch	*on the table*
neben der Tür	*near/next to the door*

Oft benutzte Wörter • High-frequency words

weil	*because*
sein/seine	*his*
ihr/ihre	*her*
zu	*too*
sehr	*very*
ziemlich	*quite, fairly*
ein bisschen	*a bit*
nicht	*not*
haben	*to have*
sein	*to be*
in	*in*
an	*at, by, on (wall)*
auf	*on (top of)*
neben	*near, next to*
heute	*today*
morgen	*tomorrow*
vor	*before*
nach	*after*

1 In der Stadt (Seiten 98–99)

1 Write sentences to say what there is and isn't in the town.

1 Es gibt hier _____ .

2 Hier gibt es _____ .

3 In der Stadt gibt es _____ .

4 Es gibt _____ hier.

Grammatik

der→einen/keinen   **die**→eine/keine   **das**→ein/kein

---

2 Read the texts. Tick the things there are in each person's town and cross the things there aren't.

Monika
> *Ich wohne in Celle. Meine Stadt ist nicht sehr groß. Es gibt hier ein Schloss und auch einen Marktplatz. Leider gibt es kein Schwimmbad und auch keine Kegelbahn.*

leider = unfortunately

Erik
> *Die Touristen kommen gern nach Verden, weil es eine Kirche und auch einen Marktplatz gibt. Ein Schloss gibt es auch, aber leider gibt es kein Schwimmbad und keine Imbissstube.*

Aisha
> *Ich wohne in Neustadt, in der Nähe vom Titisee. Neustadt ist ganz klein, aber sehr schön. Es gibt hier kein Schloss, keine Kegelbahn und leider auch kein Kino. Wir haben aber einen Bahnhof, eine Kirche und auch einen alten Marktplatz. Wir haben kein Schwimmbad, aber man kann im Sommer im Titisee schwimmen!*

Monika								
Erik								
Aisha								

3 Write two or three sentences about what there is to do where you live, as well as what there isn't. Use the texts in exercise 2 to help you.

2 wir gehen einkaufen! (Seiten 100–101)

1 Write what the customers in the souvenir shop would like. Start your sentences with *Ich möchte.*

1 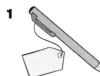 **2** **3** **4** **5**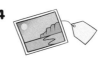

6 **7** **8**

> Look at the vocabulary on page 57 if you need to check which words to use.

1   Ich möchte einen Kuli. _____   **5** _____

2 _____   **6** _____

3 _____   **7** _____

4 _____   **8** _____

2 Complete the dialogue with words from the cloud below. Then number the lines of the conversation in the correct order 1–11.

☐ Guten Tag! _____ ich dir helfen?

☐ Welche _____ ? Wir haben blau, rot oder schwarz.

☐ Ja, klar! Dieser _____ , zum Beispiel, kostet nur €18,95.

☐ Super!

☐ Danke. Auf _____ .

☐ Sonst noch etwas?

☐ Alles _____ kostet das €38,95.

☐ Guten Tag! Ich möchte ein Souvenir _____ , vielleicht ein Kuscheltier. Haben Sie _____ ?

☐ Bitte sehr.

☐ Ja. Ich möchte ein _____ für meine Schwester.

☐ Schwarz, bitte. Wie viel _____ das?

> zusammen   Elefant   Kuscheltiere
> Wiedersehen   Kann
> kostet   Fußballtrikot   kaufen
> Farbe

3 Mmm, lecker! (Seiten 102–103)

1 Write four short conversations between hungry customers and the owner of the snack stand. The price of each individual item is shown: don't forget to add up the total price.

1  × 1   × 1

drei Euro zehn   zwei Euro fünfunddreißig

2 × 2  × 2

zwei Euro sechzig   zwei Euro fünfundzwanzig

3 × 3   × 1

drei Euro zwanzig   ein Euro neunzig

4 × 4   × 1

drei Euro fünfundneunzig   zwei Euro zehn

Ich möchte …/Ich hätte gern …	I'd like …
Das kostet alles zusammen …	All together that costs …

1   Guten Tag! Ich möchte einmal Hamburger und einmal Bratwurst, bitte.

   Das kostet alles zusammen € …

2 _____

_____

3 _____

_____

4 _____

_____

2 Write a short review of the menu, saying what there is to eat and drink and what you do and don't like.

Hamburger
Bratwurst
Pommes
Salat
Eis
Tee
Cola
Mineralwasser

Man kann … trinken/essen.	You can eat/drink …
Ich esse/trinke gern …	I like eating/drinking …
Ich esse/trinke nicht gern …	I don't like eating/drinking …
Ich mag …	I like ….
Ich mag nicht …	I don't like …..

_____

_____

_____

1 Circle the correct option to complete each sentence from the choices given. Then write the missing words in the gaps.

1 Ich _____ im See baden.

   a wirst   **b** werden   **c** werde

2 Wir werden im _____ schwimmen.

   a Meer   **b** windsurfen   **c** Bratwurst

3 _____ du nach Innsbruck fahren?

   a Wird   **b** Wirst   **c** Bist

4 Er _____ nicht nach Hannover _____ .

   a werden; fahre   **b** kann; fährt   **c** wird; fahren

5 Tobi _____ in den _____ nach Portugal fahren.

   a werde; Park   **b** wird; Bahnhof   **c** wird; Sommerferien

6 Wohin _____ wir _____ ?

   a werden; gehen   **b** kann; gehen   **c** darf; fahren

2 Read the sentences and write the correct words from the cloud in the gaps. There are more words than you need.

1 Ich werde eine Kappe _____ meinen Vater kaufen.

2 Ich _____ ein Trikot kaufen.

3 In den _____ fahren wir nach Rom.

4 Es _____ ein Schwimmbad und ein Kino in Walsrode.

5 Wir _____ nach Magdeburg fahren.

6 Ich möchte in den Bergen _____ gehen.

> für
> gibt
> möchte
> nächste Woche
> Sommerferien
> wandern
> werde
> werden

3 Write about your plans for the summer holidays. Use the questions and illustrations to help you.

- Wohin wirst du fahren?   Kiel

- Wer kommt mit?

- Was wirst du dort machen?

- Was wird dein Bruder / deine Schwester machen

- Wirst du Souvenirs kaufen?

Stimmt! 1 © Pearson Education Limited 2013

1 Rewrite each sentence. Swap the adjective in bold for an alternative adjective with a similar meaning.

1 Das Mozart Museum ist **faszinierend**. _____

2 Der Marktplatz ist **historisch**. _____

3 Das Schwimmbad ist **modern**.

_____

4 Die Kegelbahn ist **toll**. _____

2 Join up the sentence halves to describe a trip to Vienna.

1 In den Sommerferien werde

2 Dort gibt es einen

3 Am Montag kann

4 Ich finde

5 Wir werden vier

a Tage in Wien bleiben.

b ich nach Wien fahren.

c Wien fantastisch.

d Marktplatz, aber keinen See.

e man das Mozart Museum besuchen.

Now rewrite the sentences, varying the sentence structure. Remember that in German you always need the verb as the second idea.

Example: **1** Ich werde in den Sommerferien ...

3 Read the text about Hahndorf. Try to work out what the words in bold mean from the context. If you can't work out the meanings, look them up in a dictionary.

Hahndorf ist eine kleine Stadt in Südaustralien, in der Nähe von Adelaide. Es gibt dort deutsche **Einwanderer**. Die Stadt ist klein, aber **fein**! Hahndorf ist toll für Kinder und auch für **Erwachsene**. Dort gibt es viele deutsche Restaurants und Cafés. Am Mittwoch und am Sonntag gibt es immer einen Markt auf dem Marktplatz. Man kann hier Schokolade, **Kuchen** und **Kleidung** kaufen. **Wein** aus der Region kann man auch dort trinken. Ich werde **nächstes Jahr** mit meiner Schule nach Hahndorf fahren.

Hahndorf

4 Write about a city or town of your choice. Adapt some of the words and phrases from the text in exercise 3.

Remember to include: the future tense, opinions, linking words, qualifiers, frequency expressions and inverted word order.

Wiederholung 1

1 Decide which souvenir you would buy for each person and write the price in words.

Grammatik

der → er   die → sie   das → es

 Remember, *der* changes to *den* for masculine nouns.

1 Meine Mutter: _Ich werde die Tasse für meine Mutter kaufen. Sie kostet sieben Euro_
fünfundfünfzig.

2 Onkel Karl: _____

3 Meine Schwester: _____

4 Meine Freundin: _____

5 Frau Roberts: _____

2 Peter is in the tourist office in Munich. Read the dialogue, then answer the questions in full German sentences.

Tourist guide:

Guten Tag! Willkommen in München!

Hier gibt es viel zu tun! Man kann in München alles sehen!

Natürlich! Er heißt Marienplatz. Er ist sehr groß und total schön.

Also ... nicht direkt in München, aber in der Nähe von hier kann man sehr gut Ski fahren.

Ja, das gibt es! Es heißt *Robertos*. Dort kann man gut Pizza essen.

Peter:

Guten Tag! Danke schön! Was gibt es hier in München?

Gibt es hier einen Marktplatz?

Wunderbar! Und kann man in München Ski fahren?

Super. Und gibt es hier ein gutes Restaurant? Ich möchte gern Pizza essen.

Vielen Dank. Ich werde im Restaurant *Robertos* essen. Auf Wiedersehen!

1 Was kann man in München machen?
2 Wie heißt der Marktplatz?
3 Wie ist er?
4 Wo kann man Ski fahren?
5 Was möchte Peter essen?
6 Was ist *Robertos*?

Stimmt! 1 © Pearson Education Limited 2013

Wiederholung 2

1 **Rewrite the sentences in the future tense. Identify the subject to help you change the form of *werden*.**

1 Wir tauchen im Meer. _Wir werden im Meer tauchen._

2 Wir baden im See. _____

3 Ich gehe an den Strand. _____

4 Lena und Michael klettern am Samstag in den Bergen.

_____

5 Er kauft ein Kuscheltier für seine kleine Schwester.

_____

6 Kaufst du eine Kappe als Souvenir? _____

7 Wir gehen am Wochenende mit meinen Freunden einkaufen.

_____

2 **Read the postcard and answer the questions in full German sentences.**

> Liebe Oma und Lieber Opa!
>
> Hallo aus Mallorca in Spanien! Wir bleiben zwei Wochen hier, weil wir Sommerferien haben. Es gibt hier alles – einen Wasserpark, ein Schloss und auch einen Markt. Jeden Tag schwimmen wir im Meer. Im Hotel gibt es ein Schwimmbad und wir schwimmen auch hier. Man kann windsurfen und auch tauchen. Mallorca ist auch für das Essen sehr bekannt.
>
> Nächste Woche werden wir in den Bergen klettern. Ich möchte auch segeln. Ich werde auch Souvenirs kaufen!
>
> Alles Liebe,
>
> Tamika

1 Warum ist Tamika in Spanien? _____

2 Was gibt es in Mallorca? _____

3 Was kann man machen? _____

4 Ist Mallorca bekannt für das Museum? _____

5 Was wird Tamika nächste Woche machen? _____

3 **Write four true/false statements in English about the text in exercise 2. Then ask a friend to write 'True' or 'False' next to each statement.**

Example: The postcard is to Tamika's parents. False

Grammatik (Seiten 112–113)

1 **Rewrite the sentences to make them negative.**

> Use *keinen/keine/kein* to say what there is or isn't. Use *nicht* to say what you can't or don't like doing.

1 Es gibt in Düsseldorf einen Marktplatz.

_____

2 Er mag Wasserball.

_____

3 Beni kann Fußball spielen, weil er einen Ball hat.

_____

4 In der Stadt gibt es ein Kino und auch eine Kirche.

_____

5 Man darf hier schwimmen. _____

2 **Write the different forms of *möchten* in the table.**

ich		wir	
du		ihr	
er/sie/es		Sie	
		sie	

möchten
möchte
möchten
möchtest
möchte
möchtet
möchten

Complete the sentences by writing the correct form of *möchten* in each gap. Then translate the sentences into English.

1 _____ du ein Schokoladeneis?

2 Nein, aber ich _____ gern ein Vanilleeis.

3 Anne _____ nach Kapstadt in Südafrika fahren.

4 _____ ihr auch nach Windhuk in Namibia fahren?

5 Wir _____ zweimal Salat und zweimal Mineralwasser, bitte.

6 Frau Winkelmann, _____ Sie eine Tasse Tee?

3 **Fill in the gaps to complete the different forms of *werden*.**

ich __e__de   wir we__ de__

du w__r__t   ihr __er__e__

er/sie/es __ir__   Sie/sie w__r__en

4 **Write sentences about what you and your family/friends will do on your next holiday.**

Example: Ich werde jeden Tag in Frankreich wandern. Mein Bruder ... /Steffi ...

Jahresbilanz

Record your levels for *Kapitel* 5.

Listening	I have reached Level _____ in **Listening**.
Speaking	I have reached Level _____ in **Speaking**.
Reading	I have reached Level _____ in **Reading**.
Writing	I have reached Level _____ in **Writing**.

Look back through your workbook and note down the level you achieved in each skill by the end of each *Kapitel*.

	Listening	Speaking	Reading	Writing
1 Meine Welt und ich				
2 Familie und Tiere				
3 Freizeit – juhu!				
4 Schule ist klasse!				
5 Gute Reise!				

You now have a record of your progress in German for the whole year.

In der Stadt • In town

Es gibt ...	There is ... / There are ...
Es gibt ein/eine/einen ...	There is/are a ...
Es gibt kein/keine/ keinen ...	There isn't/aren't ...
in der Nähe von ...	near to
in der Nähe ...	nearby
der Bahnhof(¨e)	railway station(s)
der Imbiss(-e)/die Imbissstube(-n)	snack stand(s)
die Kegelbahn(-en)	bowling alley(s)
das Kino(-s)	cinema(s)
die Kirche(-n)	church(es)
der Marktplatz(¨e)	market square(s)
der Park(-s)	park(s)
das Schloss(¨er)	castle(s)
das Schwimmbad(¨er)	swimming pool(s)
die Eisbahn(-en)	ice rink(s)
der Fischmarkt(¨e)	fish market(s)
das Kindertheater(-)	children's theatre(s)
der Radweg(-e)	cycle path(s)
das Sportzentrum (die Sportzentren)	sports centre (sports centres)
der Stadtpark(-s)	city/town park(s)
der Wasserpark(-s)	water park(s)

Verkaufsgespräch • Sales conversation

Ich gehe einkaufen.	I am going shopping.
Ich möchte ...	I would like ...
Ich möchte ... kaufen.	I would like to buy ...
Haben Sie ...?	Do you have ...?
Kann ich dir helfen?	Can I help you?
Sonst noch etwas?	Anything else?
alles zusammen	all together

Souvenirs • Souvenirs

der Aufkleber	sticker
das Freundschafts- band	friendship bracelet
die Kappe	(baseball) cap
der Kuli	biro
das Kuscheltier	cuddly toy
die Postkarte	postcard
der Schlüsselanhänger	key ring
die Tasse	mug/cup
das Trikot	(football) shirt
Wie viel kostet ...?	How much does ... cost?
Wie viel kostet das?	How much does it cost?
Es kostet €16.	It costs 16 Euros.

Snacks und Getränke kaufen • Buying snacks and drinks

die Bratwurst	fried sausage
der Hamburger	hamburger
die Pizza	pizza
die Pommes	chips
der Salat	salad
das Eis	ice cream
die Cola	cola
das Mineralwasser	mineral water
der Tee	tea
das Fleisch	meat
der Ketchup	ketchup
die Mayo(nnaise)/ Majonäse	mayo(nnaise)
der Senf	mustard
Ich möchte einmal/ zweimal/dreimal ...	I would like one/two/ three ...
Ich hätte gern ...	I would like ...
Das macht €8.	That's €8.
Ich esse ... gern.	I like eating ... .
Ich trinke ... gern.	I like drinking ... .

Stimmt! 1 © Pearson Education Limited 2013

Wörter

In den Sommerferien
• During the summer holidays

Was wirst du machen?	*What will you do?*
Ich werde ...	*I will ...*
Wir werden ...	*We will ...*
klettern	*climb*
im Meer schwimmen	*swim in the sea*
rodeln	*toboggan*
im See baden	*bathe in the lake*
segeln	*sail*
an den Strand gehen	*go to the beach*
tauchen	*dive*
wandern	*hike*
windsurfen	*windsurf*
Was kann man dort machen?	*What can you do there?*
Man kann ... besuchen.	*'One'/People/ You can visit ...*
Die Stadt ist bekannt für ...	*The town is well known for ...*
Ich werde (eine Woche) bleiben.	*I will stay (for a week).*

Oft benutzte Wörter
• High-frequency words

am Montag	*on Monday*
am Dienstag	*on Tuesday*
am Mittwoch	*on Wednesday*
am Donnerstag	*on Thursday*
am Freitag	*on Friday*
am Wochenende	*at the weekend*
sehr	*very*
nicht sehr	*not very*
ziemlich	*quite*
immer	*always*
nicht immer	*not always*
oft	*often*
nicht oft	*not often*
nie	*never*
alles	*everything*
dort	*there*
teuer	*expensive*

Level descriptors

Listening

Level 1	I can understand some familiar spoken words and phrases.
Level 2	I can understand a range of familiar spoken phrases.
Level 3	I can understand the main points of short spoken passages and note people's answers to questions.
Level 4	I can understand the main points of spoken passages and some of the detail.
Level 5	I can understand the main points and opinions in spoken passages about different topics. I can recognise if people are speaking about the future **OR** the past as well as the present.

Speaking

Level 1	I can say single words and short phrases.
Level 2	I can answer simple questions and use set phrases.
Level 3	I can ask questions and use short phrases to answer questions about myself.
Level 4	I can take part in conversations. I can express my opinions. I can use grammar to change phrases to say something new.
Level 5	I can give short talks, in which I express my opinions. I can take part in conversations giving information, opinions and reasons. I can speak about the future **OR** the past as well as the present.

Level descriptors

Reading

Level 1	I can understand familiar words and phrases.
Level 2	I can understand familiar phrases. I can read aloud familiar words and phrases. I can use a vocabulary list to check meanings.
Level 3	I can understand the main points and people's answers to questions in short written texts.
Level 4	I can understand the main points in short texts and some of the detail. Sometimes I can work out the meaning of new words.
Level 5	I can understand the main points and opinions in texts about different topics. I can recognise if the texts are about the future **OR** the past as well as the present.

Writing

Level 1	I can write or copy single words correctly.
Level 2	I can copy short sentences correctly and write some words from memory.
Level 3	I can answer questions about myself. I can write short phrases from memory. I can write short sentences with help.
Level 4	I can write short texts on familiar topics. I can use grammar to change phrases to write something new.
Level 5	I can write short texts on a range of familiar topics. I can write about the future **OR** the past as well as the present.

Notes

Notes